Duke the Deaf Dog
ASL Series
Workbooks 1-4

Lesson Plans & Worksheets Ages 6-9

Illustrations by Theresa Murray and Caterina Baldi

Photographs by Robert Chadwick of Robert Chadwick Photography

Book cover design by Melissa Williams Design

Supplemental video material available from kellybrakenhoff.com

ISBN 9781957938059 (paperback)

ASL Videos

Also By Kelly Brakenhoff

web bookstore

DUKE THE DEAF DOG ASL SERIES

FARTS
MAKE
NOISE

DUKE THE DEAF DOG ASL SERIES

MY DAWG KOA

SOMETIMES I LIKE THE QUIET

Duke the Deaf Dog ASL Series
©2022 Caterina Baldi, illustrator
KELLYBRAKENHOFF.COM

"Never Mind"
is NOT
allowed

In the morning,
I ate my cereal.

Thunderstorms don't bother me.
Do any noises bother you?

My brother made us deputies
and we searched for outlaws.

We have a **secret** handshake.

21

Duke the Deaf Dog ASL Series
©2022 Caterina Baldi, Illustrator

Never Mind Lesson Plan Ages 6-9
By Abbey Andress, M.S.
Teacher of Deaf & Hard of Hearing Students

Whole Group (Time Frame: 20-30 Minutes)
Topic: Duke the Deaf Dog, Never Mind
Age Level: 6 Years - 9 Years

Goals:
1a: To teach the social emotional impact of being left out of conversations.
1b: To teach the importance of inclusive practices with peers.

Objectives:
Students will be able to state ways to include peers.
Students will be able to do the signs presented in the book.
Students will be able to state the emotional impact of being left out.

Essential Question: How can we be a kind friend?

Lesson Plan Format:

Engage:
Ask the students what makes them sad or upset. Allow for multiple responses.
Then, ask if anyone knows what it means to be left out? Allow for responses.
-*Wait to explain the meaning of being left out.*

Explain:
Today, we are going to read about Duke who is a Deaf dog. Who knows what Deaf means? *Allow response.*
"When someone is Deaf, it means their ears do not hear sounds like hearing people do. As we read, I want you to think about Duke and how he feels. Duke's parents and brothers all can hear, except Duke."

Alternative Plan: You may have students watch the ASL version of the story.
[https://www.youtube.com/watch?v=H4fkWfJFYhM]
Pause the story at the appropriate times and discuss the following as you would if you were reading it.

ASL Videos

Read: Pgs. 1-5
Pg. 2: Stop and show students the sign for friend. If you have a Deaf or Hard of Hearing student, talk with them ahead of time and ask if they would like to teach their friends the signs in the book. Continue throughout the story teaching the signs
[[https://youtu.be/s1hK8u0ErDQ]

Continue reading.
After you read page 5, ask students, "How do you think Duke feels now?"

Read pgs. 6-9. Ask the students to share with a partner, "Have you ever missed what someone said? Or didn't hear them? Tell them two things: How did it feel? How did you respond?"

Read pgs. 10-13. *Think, Pair, Share these questions one at a time:* "Why do you think Duke is mad?" Allow for answers. "What are some kind things the other kids could do instead of stare and point?"

Read pgs. 14-19.
Think, Pair, Share. State, "What do you think Duke is feeling right now? Why is that?"
"I want you to take a second to think, 'How can we make Duke feel more included with his friends?"

-Ideas to add: Have him look at you when you talk. Make the room quieter, and make sure he's included. Ask him to go with you to a quieter place and chat. Be visual.

Read pgs. 20-24. *Discussion:*
"Who can remind me what the big rule is?"
"What is something they ALWAYS do if he asks, "What did you say?"
"Why is it important to include everyone and be a kind friend?"
"Absolutely! We are all people, and we all need friends. We need to be kind to everyone! No matter what!"

Conclusion and Reflection:
Teach students the various meanings of saying, "never mind" in ASL with this video of Amy Willman.
https://www.youtube.com/watch?v=IdG1AI_LRcM

Extra:
Tell a friend why we should not tell someone, "Never mind."

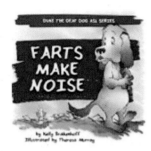

Farts Make Noise Lesson Plan Ages 6-9

By Abbey Andress, M.S.
Teacher of Deaf & Hard of Hearing Students

Whole Group (Time Frame: 30-40 Minutes)
Topic: Duke the Deaf Dog, Farts Make Noise
Age Level: 6 Years - 9 Years

Goals:
1a: To teach about sounds that students may be unaware of.
1b: To discuss the pros of having a hearing difference.

Objectives:
Students will be able to state sounds that are loud or quiet, and some sounds that are not polite.
Students will be able to do the signs presented in the book.
Students will be able to state how being Deaf or Hard of Hearing can be positive.

Essential Question: How do noises affect Deaf or Hard of Hearing people?

Lesson Plan Format:
Engage:
Ask the students, "What noises do you like?" *Allow for multiple responses.* "This book is called, *Farts Make Noise*. What a silly name! I wonder why the author called it that? Take a minute to think about why you believe Kelly Brakenhoff decided to title her book, *Farts Make Noise*."

Explain:
"Today, we are going to read about Duke who is a Deaf dog. Who knows what Deaf means?" *Allow for multiple responses.* "When someone is Deaf, it means their ears do not hear sounds like hearing people do. Duke's parents and brothers all can hear, except Duke. As we read, I want you to think about sounds you hear every day in your life."

Alternative Plan: You may have students watch the ASL version of the story.
https://youtu.be/w_fMBnGlGMs Pause the story at the appropriate times and discuss the following as you would if you were reading it.

Read: Pgs. 1-5
Pg. 1: Stop and show students signs. If you have a Deaf or Hard of Hearing student, talk with them ahead of time and ask if they would like to teach their friends the signs in the book. Continue throughout the story teaching the signs. https://youtu.be/I2yoYLvb78U

Read pgs. 1-3:
Ask the students, "What noises was Duke making?" "Does that sound bother you?"

ASL Videos

Read pgs.4-5:
You may use this opportunity to share a repeating noise that you may be in the habit of. For example, "Sometimes, we make repeating noises without even realizing it! I always click pens. My husband gets very annoyed, but I do not even realize I'm doing it!" Ask: "Is there something you do sometimes? Tapping a pencil, kicking your feet on the desk? Tell me one thing you may do." *Wait for responses.*

Read pgs. 6-7:
Ask, "I notice the author said the fire alarms were flashing. Why do you think fire alarms flash?" *Allow for multiple responses.* Explain: "Fire alarms flash in case you do not hear it. The flashing will catch your attention so you can leave safely."

Read pgs. 8-13:
State, "Wow! Now we know why the author titled the book, *Farts Make Noise*. It's because she wanted to really capture your attention and to give you a hint about something you may learn about. *Think, Pair, Share:* How did Duke react when he learned about farts making noise?" *Allow for responses.* "He laughed! Sometimes we have to laugh at things that might be embarrassing like learning someone heard you accidentally pass gas." State, "Everyone needs to learn which noises are not polite, right?"

Read pgs. 14-16:
"What does bother mean?" *Allow for responses.* "Yes, it means to annoy someone with something they do not like. Why do you think it did not bother Duke when his brother burped? I want you to think, pair, share with a partner and tell them why it didn't bother Duke when his brother burped." *Allow time. Have partners share out answers.* "Why might that be a good thing?" *Allow for responses.*

Read pgs. 18-21:
"Who remembers what doesn't make noise and doesn't bother anyone?" *Allow time for responses.* "Right! After you learned that, when would be some really good times to use sign language rather than voice?" *Allow for responses. Ideas to add:* underwater, church, secrets, across big rooms, through windows.

Read pgs. 22-26:
Think, Pair, Share: "What noises bother you?" *Allow for multiple responses.* "When I think about not being woken up by thunder, or hearing burps, or all of those annoying noises, do you think it can be a positive, or good, thing to be Deaf?" *Allow for responses. Ideas to add: Deaf and hard of hearing people who use ASL gain access to a different language, a community of other deaf individuals, and a way of experiencing the world visually. Explain that Deaf people still have to pay attention to the noises they make.*

Conclusion and Reflection:
Students will watch this ASL Deaf Culture lesson by Amy Willman on Deaf Etiquette. (7 minutes) (https://youtu.be/uUANMro3J_U *Share with a friend or the full class one thing they learned from the Deaf Culture video.*

Extra:
Students can tell a friend when/why it can be a positive thing to have a hearing difference.
Students can write about how noises affect Deaf people.

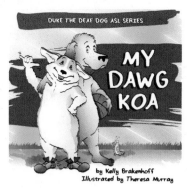

DUKE THE DEAF DOG ASL SERIES

MY DAWG KOA

by Kelly Brakenhoff
Illustrated by Theresa Murray

My Dawg Koa Lesson Plan Ages 6-9
By Abbey Andress, M.S.
Teacher of Deaf & Hard of Hearing Students

Whole Group (Time Frame: 30-45 Minutes)
Topic: Duke the Deaf Dog, My Dawg Koa
Age Level: 6 Years - 9 Years

Goals:

1a: To teach diversity among friends.

1b: To discuss the tools a person who is Deaf or hard of hearing can use.

Objectives:

Students will be able to state how Koa and Duke are the same.

Students will be able to state how Koa and Duke are different.

Students will be able to show tools Koa and Duke use.

Essential Question: How are some people the same and different?

Lesson Plan Format:

Engage:

Ask the students, "Who has brown hair?" *Allow for multiple responses.* "So a few of you. Who has blonde hair?" "Who has glasses?" *Point out similarities and differences.* Have them say what is the same about them and a friend next to them. "All of us are the same in some ways and different in other ways."

Explain:

"Today, we are going to read about Duke who is a Deaf dog and his friend, Koa who is also Deaf. Who here has a friend?" *Allow for multiple responses.* "What do you like to do with your friends?" *Allow for answers.* "Are we all the exact same as our friends?" *Allow for answers.* "As we read, I want you to think about Duke and Koa. What is the same about them? What is different? What is the same and different about their families? This book is called, *My Dawg Koa.* Look at Koa here, and Duke here. What do you see that is the same about them?" Answers: they are both dogs, they both have ears, color, etc. "What do you see that is different?" *Allow for answers.* Koa has a cochlear implant, Duke has a hearing aid, dog breed is different.

Alternative Plan: You may have students watch the ASL version of the story . https://youtu.be/v1Ip-7j5Z_I Pause the story at the appropriate times and discuss the following as you would if you were reading it.

Read together:

Pg 1: Stop and show students signs. If you have a Deaf or Hard of Hearing student, talk with them ahead of time and ask if they would like to teach their friends the signs in the book. Continue throughout the story teaching the signs. https://youtu.be/3goUBNcF7q0

Read pgs. 1-5:

"Koa is afraid of spiders. Is Duke afraid of them?" "What is something you are afraid of?" *Allow for answers. Share what you as the teacher are afraid of and what a friend may be afraid of.*

Read pgs. 6-10:
Ask, "Are they really good cleaners?"
"No, they are so messy! Is that the same or different from you?" *Allow for answers.*

Read pgs. 11-12:
Ask, "What are captions?" *Allow for answers, if they don't know, continue:* "If I look closely, I can see some words on the TV. Closed captions are words that are typed out so that we can read what someone is saying. People who are Deaf or hard of hearing use captions to understand what people are saying on TV. Other people who are hearing like captions too!"

Read pgs. 13-16:
"What does Koa's doorbell do that is different from Duke's?" Answers: it flashes lights so they can see someone rang the doorbell.

Read pgs. 16-26:
"What is different about Koa and Duke's family?" Koa's family is Deaf, flashing lights, vibrating alarms, video phone, different dog breeds.

Read pgs. 26-End:
"So, even though Duke and Koa are different, they are still friends!" "Duke and Koa do have a lot in common, too. Do you think we should be friends with people that are different from us? Yes!"

Conclusion and Reflection:
"Tell a friend why it's good to be friends with people even when they are different from us."

Activity:
"Koa and Dawg love to have fun with toys. Sometimes they played with toys someone got from a store. Sometimes they were home made toys. One toy we can make only needs one thing, paper! We can make paper hats and even boats and lots more things. Has anyone made any toys from paper before?" *Allow for answers.*
"Today, we will make a hat."

Directions on next page.

ASL Videos

Make a Paper Hat!

For best results use a newspaper or store sales flyer
larger than a regular sheet of paper.

1 Start with newspaper folded in half the way it comes.

2 Fold right and left corners to the middle to form a point.

3 Open the bottom and fold up the front and back.

4 Tuck the corners over the fold to the back and front. Add tape to make it sturdy.

5 Open it up and shape the hat to fit your head

6 Fold up the bottom edge all around for a pirate hat.

Also works as a boat!

©2021 kellybrakenhoff.com

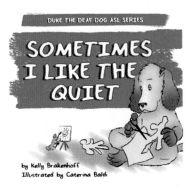

DUKE THE DEAF DOG ASL SERIES

SOMETIMES I LIKE THE QUIET

by Kelly Brakenhoff
Illustrated by Caterina Baldi

Sometimes I Like the Quiet Lesson Plan Ages 6-9
By Abbey Andress, M.S.
Teacher of Deaf & Hard of Hearing Students

Whole Group (Time Frame: 30-45 Minutes)
Topic: Duke the Deaf Dog, Sometimes I Like the Quiet
Age Level: 6 Years - 9 Years

GOALS:
1a: Some things are harder for others.
1b: To discuss how a Deaf or hard of hearing person uses all of their senses to "listen."

OBJECTIVES:
Students will be able to state how people who are Deaf or hard of hearing "listen."
Students will be able to state why Duke gets tired.

Essential Question: What can make people tired?

LESSON PLAN FORMAT:
Engage:
Ask the students, "What do you think is hard work?" Allow for multiple responses. "Sometimes, what may be hard for us is easy for others." Give an example related to you.

Explain:
Today, we are going to read about Duke who is a Deaf dog. Duke wears a hearing aid during school and at home. Who knows what a hearing aid is? Allow for multiple responses. This book is called, Sometimes I like the Quiet. Do you like quiet or noisy? Allow for multiple responses. Let's see what Duke likes!

Alternative Plan: You may have students watch the ASL version of the story.
Pause the story at the appropriate times and discuss the following as you would if you were reading it.

Read: Pgs 1-3
Pg 1: Stop and show students signs. If you have a Deaf or Hard of Hearing student, talk with them ahead of time and ask if they would like to teach their friends the signs in the book. Continue throughout the story teaching the signs. https://youtu.be/NGJKH0V3UpA

"How does Duke use his eyes to listen as well?" Allow for multiple responses. "Does seeing who is talking help you, too?" Allow for multiple responses. "Duke says that listening is hard work. Why do you think that is?" Allow for multiple responses. Expand if needed and make clarifications.

ASL Videos

Read pgs. 4-5:

"Does it get noisy in our (your) classroom sometimes?" Allow for multiple responses. "Think about when it's noisy. Does it make it harder to hear your friends or your teachers?" Allow for multiple responses. "When someone has a hearing aid, they have to work harder to listen."

Read pgs. 6-9:

"What does it mean to listen with your eyes?" Allow for answers. (Watch for gestures like pointing, shrugging shoulders, facial expressions, what are other people in the room doing?)
"Do deaf and hard of hearing people listen with their eyes?" (sign language, body language) "Do people who can hear also listen with their eyes?"

Read pgs. 10-17: "Why is Duke feeling sad?" Allow for multiple responses. "Exactly! Duke is Deaf and uses a hearing aid which is helpful, but is a lot of work to use. Duke is tired after working all day to listen.

"Duke got in trouble because his mom thought he didn't listen. He was watching TV and didn't hear her. Do you ever get in trouble for not listening?" Allow for multiple responses.

Read pgs. 18-19:

Ask, "How did Duke's Dad say he would help him?" Allow for multiple responses. "Are there things you like to do when you are tired? I like to lay down for a bit on the couch." Allow for multiple responses. "Just like you, Duke likes to rest from having to listen by taking his hearing aid off sometimes."

Read pgs. 20-END: Ask, "Do you like the quiet sometimes, too?" Allow for multiple responses. That is the end of the book! Who remembers why Duke gets tired?" Allow for multiple responses.

Conclusion and Reflection:
"Tell a friend what else Duke used to help him '"listen.'"

Activity:
The activity is a game of red light, green light. There is a version of this game that is played in the Deaf Culture. Instead of saying, "Red light," or, "Green light," the person who is it, turns away from the people playing and then will, at their choosing, turn around quickly. Once they turn around, the runners have to freeze. The person who does it will call out anyone who they see moving.

Activity: Watch the story read in ASL
https://www.youtube.com/watch?v=o08KPZwXheU

ASL Videos

Writing & ASL Practice

Write each word in English and practice making the ASL sign.

Noisy

Eat

Mother

Father

Writing & ASL Practice

Write each word in English and practice making the ASL sign.

Friend

Line

Play

Walk

Laugh

Farts Make Noise
Writing & ASL Practice

Write each word in English and practice making the ASL sign.

Morning

School

Bother

Fire drill

Butterfly

Stink

Smell

Excuse me

Movie

Carefully

Lightning

Quiet

My Dawg Koa
Writing & ASL Practice

Write each word in English and practice making the ASL sign.

Secret

Spider

Forget

Help

Clean

Captions

Writing & ASL Practice
Write each word in English and practice making the ASL sign.

Cookie

Basketball

Tomato

Wait

Birthday

Sometimes I Like the Quiet
Writing & ASL Practice
Write each word in English and practice making the ASL sign.

Loud

Listen

Noisy

Dinosaur

Quiet

Hearing Aid

Action

Fair

Tired

Rude

Played

Fun

Sometimes

FEELINGS

What does it mean to be left out?
Do people who are deaf get left out sometimes because
they didn't hear what was said?
What feelings does Duke have in the book Never Mind?

"Never Mind"
is not
allowed.

Draw a face that shows Duke's
feelings when he's left out.

Draw a face that shows Duke's feelings
when he's included in conversations.

NEVER MIND

THE BIG RULE

LEFT OUT FEELINGS

INCLUDED FEELINGS

_____

_____

_____

_____

_____

_____

BE KIND

Duke doesn't like being told never mind. Take a moment to think about how you can be a kind friend to someone who feels left out or ignored. Write your answers below.

1 _____

2 _____

3 _____

4 _____

5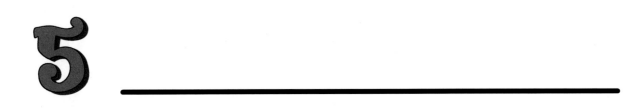

WHICH KIND OF NOISE?

Circle the correct answer for each image.

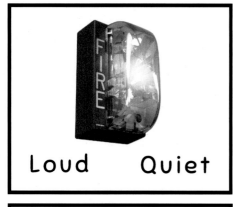

Loud   Quiet

Loud   Quiet

Loud   Quiet

Loud   Quiet

Loud   Quiet

Loud   Quiet

Loud   Quiet

Loud   Quiet

Loud   Quiet

Do any noises bother you? Write one below.

BE POSITIVE

Duke slept well the night of the storm. What are some other good things about being deaf or hard of hearing?
Write your answers below.

1 _____

2 _____

3 _____

4 _____

5 _____

I CAN COMPARE DUKE AND KOA.
Write or draw 2 things about Duke and Koa that are the same and 2 things that are different.

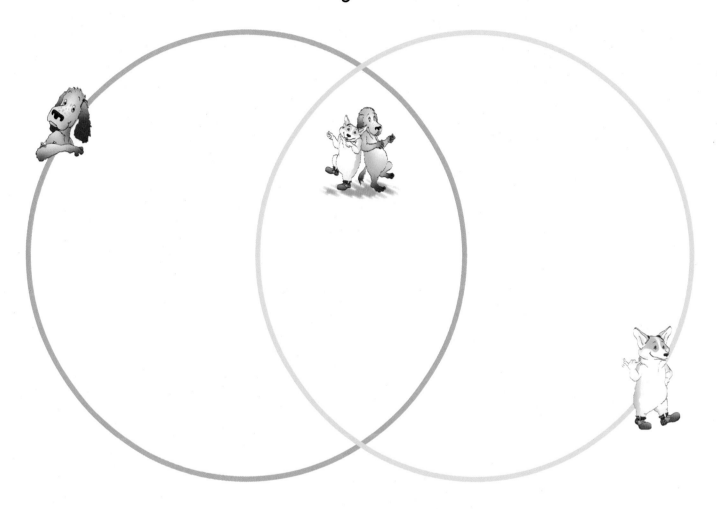

SAME, SAME, BUT DIFFERENT

How am I similar to my friends? How am I different? Draw a picture of you and a
friend, and label how you are similar and different.
Use describing words for your personality.

ME: _____

MY FRIEND:
_____

FIND THE SAME LETTERS

Draw a circle around all the letter K's you see.

K k

is for Koa

(k) r K A R z o S m b

K n L N C K T K E n S

a R K A Z H r j n q

N d L S N K T k i n U

C K o E N X f w b U G

The Missing Letter

Look at the pictures below. Say what you see out loud.
Add the missing letter on the blank.

K o _

_ a c o

D u _ e

_ o o k i e s

c a _

b _ _ k s

w o r _

_ a s k e t b a l l

c a _ e

Name: _____   Date: _____

MY DAWG KOA WORD SEARCH

Circle words in the puzzle below

L	D	E	P	T	K	B	I	R	T	H	D	A	Y
D	N	A	A	R	T	F	S	T	H	E	R	I	P
I	A	P	P	E	O	L	R	S	W	O	R	D	E
F	E	W	E	E	M	S	P	I	D	E	R	O	F
F	L	E	R	H	A	S	S	E	E	H	O	K
E	C	R	H	O	T	S	E	A	T	N	D	L	C
R	K	O	A	U	O	O	A	E	P	L	D	F	O
E	A	K	T	S	E	A	G	M	T	A	S	S	O
N	M	O	K	E	S	R	D	A	E	D	O	E	K
T	O	I	A	C	O	U	C	S	A	D	D	C	I
T	V	K	P	F	H	O	D	U	K	E	O	R	E
K	I	D	P	H	S	L	N	A	S	R	E	E	S
R	E	C	A	P	T	I	O	N	S	S	E	T	A
B	A	S	K	E	T	B	A	L	L	E	S	Y	T

FRIEND
TACOS
DUKE
TREEHOUSE
COOKIES
CAPTIONS
DIFFERENT
MOVIE
KOA
SPIDER
FORGET
BASKETBALL
TOMATOES
LADDER
BIRTHDAY
SAME
SECRET
PAPER HAT
SWORD
CLEAN

kellybrakenhoff.com

Whole body listening

Complete with the parts of the body.

Word Bank

hands
brain
feet
eyes
mouth
ears

.... are looking.

.... is paying attention.

.... is quiet.

.... are listening.

.... are still.

.... are still.

WHAT ARE YOU FEELING?

In this story, Duke has a lot of different feelings. He gets tired, sad, mad, happy, and excited. Draw a picture of what you are feeling right now.

I feel _____
_____ .

PAYING ATTENTION *challenge*

Write 2 examples of how you show how you are paying attention and how you might show you are not listening. It can be considered rude if we do not listen to others.

1. I show I am paying attention by…

_____
_____
_____
_____

2. I show I am paying attention by…

_____
_____
_____
_____

1. I might be rude if I…

_____
_____
_____
_____
_____

2. I might be rude if I…

_____
_____
_____
_____
_____

Example
I show I am listening
by answering questions
_____

Example
I might be rude if I
talk when someone else
is talking.

Word Scramble

Circle or highlight the words you find from
Sometimes I Like the Quiet.

```
H E A R I N G A I D
Z W D I N O S A U R
F A I R L I S T E N
J J P R K O T R T R
B A S K E T B A L L
Q U I E T O I U B D
D X A D P P H R Z O
E U G G A L Z Q E G
U P K W M I A V K D
M H C E Y C E Y E F
```

basketball	hearing aid	tired	duke
listen	play	quiet	fair
dinosaur	dog		

Workbook Contributors

KELLY BRAKENHOFF is an American Sign Language Interpreter whose motivation for learning ASL began in high school when she wanted to converse with her deaf friends. She divides her writing time between two series: the Cassandra Sato Mystery series for ages 12 and up and Duke the Deaf Dog ASL Series for ages 3-9. She and her husband have a German Wirehair Pointer.
Photo credit: Robert Chadwick

THERESA MURRAY has been creating custom art and murals for over 20 years. She pulls from her past as a grooming assistant to inspire the dog illustrations for this series. Theresa lives in Omaha, Nebraska with her husband, two sons, and their Westie, Tinkerbell.

Italian illustrator CATERINA BALDI is also an author, translator, and English teacher for little kids. Sometimes I Like the Quiet is her first project with us. Her grandmother became deaf as a girl following meningitis, and everyone in the house talked to her by lipreading and invented gestures known as "home signs." Caterina felt a connection with Duke's story because her mother is also deaf in one ear and doesn't like missing out on important conversations. Caterina's picture book Three Cats in the Sink was published by Settenove in May, 2022. Caterina doesn't own any pets, but the dogs and cats in her neighborhood are all her friends.

ABBEY ANDRESS (BUETTGENBACH) is a Teacher of the Deaf and Hard of Hearing in Buda, TX. She writes the lesson plans that accompany the books in the Duke series. Abbey grew up in Pierce, NE as the only Deaf person in her family. She attended the University of Nebraska - Lincoln where she earned her bachelor's and master's degrees. The two main goals for Abbey are always to be the best Deaf Educator she can be and to travel the world. Being the Coordinator for the Nebraska Transition Summit for Students who are Deaf and Hard of Hearing is Abbey's biggest achievement to date. Abbey is a proud dog mom to a black Lab named Buckley,.

ASL signs and YouTube videos in ASL feature AMY WILLMAN.
Amy has worked as an American Sign Language Coordinator and Lecturer at the University of Nebraska-Lincoln since 2001. Before moving back to her childhood home in Nebraska, Amy taught elementary school for three years and taught ASL at Santa Fe Community College for six years. Her bachelor's degree in Elementary Level and Studio Arts is from Gallaudet University, the only Deaf university in the world. She earned her master's degree in Deaf Education from McDaniel College. Amy co-authored a book with her mother, *Amy Signs: A Mother and Her Deaf Daughter, and their Stories* in 2012. She lives with her four beloved cats, three of whom are deaf.
Photo credit: Robert Chadwick

Order softcover or eBook copies of the Duke the Deaf Dog ASL Series directly from kellybrakenhoff.com, from Amazon or anywhere you normally buy books. https://amzn.to/3ikRxGe

Find Kelly online here:
- Website and blog: https://kellybrakenhoff.com/
- Sign up for monthly newsletter: https://mailchi.mp/78c3aaa46ef3/kellybrakenhoffnews
- Facebook page: https://www.facebook.com/kellybrakenhoffauthor

Download digital files

Made in United States
Orlando, FL
20 November 2023

39175354R00027